WHERE IN THE WORLD IS BOB?

Can you find Street Cat Bob on his adventures around the world?

James Bowen and Garry Jenkins
Illustrated by Steve Wiltshire

HODDER &
STOUGHTON

CONTENTS

BOB'S ADVENTURE

Hello. My name is Bob and I'm about to head off around the world with my best friend James, a London busker. I'm going to blog about my travels and the people – and cats – I meet.

We've got all the things we need: I've got my passport, a collection of my favourite scarves, my laptop and my favourite toy, scraggedy mouse. James has got his guitar and the bicycle that we ride together, the Bobmobile!

You can follow our journey if you like. All you need to do is spot us – and our items – at each destination.

Hope you have fun.
Love, Bob

THINGS TO FIND

THERE ARE LOTS OF THINGS FOR YOU TO SPOT IN EACH OF THE COUNTRIES THAT WE VISIT. HERE'S A GUIDE:

Me!

I love to visit new places and meet new people. There's nothing more fun than mingling in with the locals and becoming just a face in the crowd. Who knows, maybe that's where you will find me?

My Scarf

I love to wear warm, woolly scarves. They keep me cosy – and are colourful too. It's the same when I travel. Wherever I go, you'll find my scarf isn't far away.

My Passport

I always take my pet passport (or should that be pussport?) with me on my travels. I always keep it somewhere safe. Where? Well, that's for you to work out.

My Toy Mouse

Like all cats, I love to play, especially with my favourite toy, a little cloth animal I like to call scraggedy mouse. I take him with me everywhere. Can you spot him hiding in each picture?

James

James is my best friend and travel companion. Ever since he helped me when he found me injured, we have been inseparable. So he will be with me in every country too. If you look closely enough, you'll always see him in the picture.

James' guitar

I love to listen to James playing his guitar. So he will bring it with him to each of the countries we visit. See if you can find it.

The Bobmobile

James and I often travel around London on our bike, 'the Bobmobile'. It is coming with us on our trip as well. Can you spot where we have parked it?

My Laptop

I always write about my travels on my blog, 'Around the World in 80 Bobs'. So I carry my laptop with me. Let's hope I don't lose it. Can you keep an eye on it for me?

MY FRIENDS

In each country I am going to visit a feline friend who lives there. Look on the next page for a list of them all...

MY FELINE FRIENDS

(AND CANINE)

United Kingdom
Princess, the busking dog

Singapore
Raffles, the Singapura cat

Turkey
Gli, the museum cat

Germany
Lucifer, the Cinderella cat

China
Chan, the Great Wall stray

USA
Bob, the basketball bobcat

Brazil
Bobinho, the carnival cat

Italy
Chico, the Pope's pussycat

Japan
Maneki, the temple cat

South Africa
Sam, the serval

India
Ben, the Bengal cat

The Netherlands
Henrietta, the rescue queen

Australia
Trim, the Flinders' cat

Thailand
Mia, the Siamese cat

Canada
**Queen of the Mist,
the Niagara kitty**

Egypt
Mau, goddess of the desert

3

United Kingdom

It's time to say goodbye to the streets of London. So James and I have come to one of our favourite spots, the Piazza at Covent Garden, to sing a couple of farewell songs. We've brought one of our friends, Princess the dog, with us too. He is often with us on the streets, keeping us company. Can you spot us and our travel items?

Singapore

Singapore is known as the City of Lions. So I've come to visit the city's most famous statue, a giant statue of a lion. He looks pretty fearsome. I've also come to see Raffles, a relative of the three cats that sailed to America in the 1970s to establish the famous Singapura breed. Singapuras are known for their large eyes and ears, as well as their brown coat and stubby tail. Can you see Raffles – and the rest of us – in the crowd?

Turkey

Istanbul is famous for its souks and colourful markets. But it's also famous for its thousands of much loved street cats. The city's tradition of kindness to cats is partly drawn from the Muslim ideas of tolerance and the Prophet Muhammad's famous love for his feline friends. When American President Barack Obama came to Turkey he befriended Gli, one of the half dozen tabby cats that live at the famous Hagia Sophia museum. Can you see me and Gli in this busy souk scene?

Germany

I love Christmas, it's my favourite time of the year. So I've come to visit a Christmas market in the town of Hanau in Germany. I've come to see Lucifer, named after the famous cat in the *Cinderella* story. Hanau is home of the Brothers Grimm, who published some of the most famous fairy tales in the world – including *Cinderella* – so it's Lucifer's home too. Can you see him – and me?

China

They say you can see the Great Wall of China from space. According to some, when they built the wall, they added thousands of cat flaps. They certainly need them because the Wall is filled with hundreds – if not thousands – of stray cats. Here I am with one of them, Chan. Can you spot us?

USA

Here I am watching a basketball match in the the good old US of A. My favourite basketball team is the Charlotte Bobcats, one of the best teams in America. They are named after the bobcat, a distant relative of mine that's common in the western states. There's one of them in the crowd here. His name is Bob too. Can you find him?

Brazil

Rio de Janeiro is the carnival capital of the world. Even the cats love to party. Each year they join the city's dogs in a colourful parade and street party called the Blocao. Owners dress them up in amazing costumes and walk them along the famous Copacabana beach. Can you see me enjoying the party with my Brazilian friend Bobinho?

17

Italy

I'm hiding in St Peter's Square, amongst the crowds, waiting to see the Pope. Cats aren't allowed in the residences of the Vatican City but there are many of them at the Pope's other residence, Castel Gandolfo. Pope Benedict, the Pope who resigned in 2013, had a favourite called Chico. An earlier Pope, Pius XI, featured in a comic book, *The Cat from Castel Gandolfo*, in which he had a fictitious feline friend. See if you can spot me and Chico here?

Japan

I'm visiting a temple in Japan filled with the famous maneki-nekos, or lucky cats. According to one legend, the first lucky cat was a stray who was taken in by a poor shopkeeper, who was rewarded with good fortune after spending all his money on feeding the cat. (A bit like James, who spent all his money on making me well.) Today shops, restaurants and temples everywhere in Japan have a maneki-neko that raises its arm as a sign of good fortune. The cats also wear scarves, just like me, as well as a bell around their neck. I've come to visit a modern Japanese cat, also called Maneki. Can you see us?

21

South Africa

James and I have travelled to a safari park in South Africa to see if we can find one of my wild cousins. This part of the world is home to many of my distant relatives. A lot of you will know three of them – the lion, leopard and cheetah. But have you heard of the caracal, the African civet and the serval? Here I am, spending time with Sam the serval. Do we look like long-lost cousins?

India

Another one of my distant cousins is the Bengal cat, a cross between a domestic cat and an Asian leopard cat, named after the eastern region of India. He loves to swim in water, just like me. I'm never happier than when I'm splashing around in James's bathtub at home. Here I am at the famous Taj Mahal in India with one of my Bengal cousins, Ben. Can you find us?

The Netherlands

The Netherlands is the home of one of the world's most famous and unusual cat sanctuaries, The Cat Boat in Amsterdam. It's believed to be the only floating sanctuary in the world and was first opened in 1966. I'm here with a cat called Henrietta, who along with her abandoned kittens, was the first occupant of The Cat Boat sanctuary after being discovered by its founder, Henriette van Weelde.

Australia

I've popped down to Australia to visit Trim, Sydney's most famous cat. He was the pet of the famous explorer Matthew Flinders, who circumnavigated the country at the start of the 19th century. There's a statue of him in the city. Here I am at the famous Sydney Opera House. Can you see me and Trim?

Thailand

Thailand is famous for its love of cats. It is home to some of the world's first cat cafés. It's also the birthplace of the Siamese cat. (Thailand used to be called Siam.) I'm here in the middle of Bangkok, the capital, with a Siamese pal, Mia. Can you find us?

Meow Cat Café

Canada

Niagara Falls is one of the most famous waterfalls in the world. But not a lot of people know that the first person to go over it – and survive – was a cat. The cat belonged to the first human to go over the Falls, Annie Edson Taylor, who achieved the feat in a barrel stuffed with a mattress. Two days before she went over the Horseshoe Falls in October 1901, Annie tested the barrel by sending her cat down the rapids. The cat survived and was reunited with Annie 17 minutes after taking the plunge. What a brave kitty! Can you spot her here with me?

Egypt

Cats have been worshipped in Egypt for thousands of years. There was even a city, Bubastis, where pilgrims came to pay homage to them. I've come to the desert to see one of the most famous figures in all of ancient Egypt, the Sphinx. She's half lion, half human. I've also come to see Mau, a descendant of the Egyptian cats who were worshipped in the time of the Pharaohs. Can you spot her, me and James in this scene?

35

ANSWERS

DID YOU FIND EVERYTHING?
HERE ARE SOME HANDY HINTS TO
HELP IF YOU GOT STUCK.

UNITED KINGDOM

SINGAPORE

TURKEY

GERMANY

CHINA

USA

BRAZIL

ITALY

JAPAN

SOUTH AFRICA

INDIA

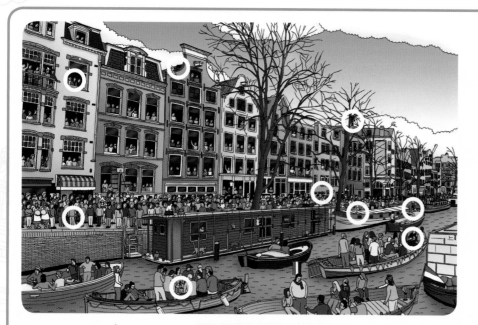

THE NETHERLANDS

AUSTRALIA

THAILAND

CANADA

EGYPT

An Hachette UK company

1

Text Copyright © James & Bob Limited and Connected Content Limited
Illustrations by Steve Wiltshire

www.stevewiltshire.co.uk

A CIP catalogue record for this title is available from the British Library

ISBN 978 1 444 78282 0

Printed and bound in Italy by L.E.G.O S.p.A.

Hodder & Stoughton policy is to use papers that are natural, renewable
and recyclable products and made from wood grown in sustainable
forests. The logging and manufacturing processes are expected to
conform to the environmental regulations of the country of origin.

Hodder & Stoughton Ltd
338 Euston Road
London NW1 3BH
www.hodder.co.uk